Euthanasia—
a Good Death?

Margaret Whipp

Consultant in Palliative Medicine
and Director of Hospice Services, Hartlepool and East Durham

Tutor in Practical Theology, Cranmer Hall, Durham

GROVE BOOKS LIMITED
RIDLEY HALL RD CAMBRIDGE CB3 9HU

Contents

1. Boundaries of Life and Death 3

2. Boundaries of Autonomy 12

3. Boundaries of Compassion 20

4. Conclusion 24

The Cover Illustration is by Peter Ashton

First Impression April 2000
ISSN 1470-854X
ISBN 1 85174 430 4

1

Boundaries of Life and Death

Dying Today

Popular demand for euthanasia intensifies year by year. Both public debate and private anguish are stirred by emotive portrayals of prolonged and avoidable suffering at the end of life. Feelings run high. Surely, with all the skill of modern medical science, something should be done to eliminate unnecessary distress? Public opinion polls show consistent support for the legalization of euthanasia in a wide range of circumstances.[1]

Attitudes to Euthanasia	
% who think euthanasia should ' definitely' or ' probably' be allowed by law for a person...	
...who has an incurable illness which leaves them unable to make a decision about their own future, for instance imagine a person in a coma or on a life-support machine who is never expected to regain consciousness (if their relatives agree).	86%
... who has an incurable and painful illness from which they will die, for example, someone dying of cancer.	80%
... in a coma, never expected to regain consciousness, but who is not on a life-support machine (if their relatives agree).	58%
... who is not in much pain, nor in danger of death, but becomes permanently and completely dependent on relatives for all their needs, for example, someone who cannot feed, wash, or go to the toilet by themselves.	51%
... with an incurable disease from which they will die, but is not very painful, as might be the case for someone dying from leukaemia.	44%
... with an incurable illness from which they will not die, for example, someone with severe arthritis.	42%
... someone who is not ill or close to death, but who is simply tired of living and wishes to die—for example, someone who is extremely lonely and no longer enjoys life.	12%

1   Source: 'Matters of Life and Death: Attitudes to Euthanasia' in *British Social Attitudes the 13th Report* (SCPR, 1996/7).

Issues of euthanasia and assisted suicide are hardly new on the ethical agenda. Yet conflicting views remain unresolved, and the debate refuses to die. Amongst church people, and in wider society, momentum for change is growing, and those who agitate for reform are no longer a dubious minority, but represent a well-organized lobby of influential and articulate opinion leaders.

What is happening to fuel the debate? Why do attitudes continue to shift away from the established moral and legal norm which prohibits euthanasia? There is no one clear explanation, but some significant factors are not difficult to identify.

First, there is a growing fear of long, lingering death. The ageing population and the expansion of degenerative disease cast a spectre of decline and decrepitude which many younger people are afraid to contemplate. Medical technology has extended the boundaries of life and death in ways unimaginable to an earlier generation. Frequent media portrayals of intensive care, and not so infrequent personal experiences of 'high-tech' prolongation of life, have raised enormous questions about the quality of a life that only continues tied to complex technology. Extreme cases, such as the Quinlan and Cruzan cases in the United States, and the Tony Bland case in Britain, have made intensely public the dilemma of keeping alive irreparably damaged bodies, beyond any reasonable expectation of return to normal life for what remains of the 'person.'

There is widespread revulsion at the medicalization of death. Death is no longer experienced as a natural part of life. People dread, as a recent article described it, 'a twilight life tethered to feeding tubes or respirators.'[2] People used to die at home, in the bosom of their families, surrounded by their own belongings and photographs and furniture. Now they die in institutions, amongst strangers and alien technology. Could euthanasia offer a kindly alternative to the ultimate facelessness of dying amidst an inhuman mass of machinery?

New threats have arisen in recent years. The AIDS epidemic has created a fearful scenario for many young people, who are appalled at the social and physical misery visited upon some of the most colourful individuals of the western world, and many vulnerable people in the third world. Might euthanasia not be a preferable solution to the inexorable degradation of this modern-day leprosy?

The experience of dying has changed in contemporary society, and so has the acceptance of suffering as a part of human life. Expectations raised by the successes of modern medicine have created a demand for swift and painless, tidily controlled death. The desire for euthanasia is not only about inadequate pain and symptom control, or inappropriate use of life-prolonging technology. The deeper dimension for many people is the desire to keep control, and the dread of losing it. Despite all the successes of the hospice movement, and the growth of expertise in pain relief and palliative care, there are many patients who resist to the uttermost any move towards dependency and loss of self-determination. This strident mood of autonomy, so characteristic of modern western societies, is the factor above all which inflames the contemporary clamour for euthanasia.

---

2   Anon, 'Final Exit: Euthanasia Guide Sells Out' in *Nature*, 1991, 352, p 553.

Definitions

Before we review the development of the euthanasia debate in recent history, some definitions will clarify the terms of the debate.

Euthanasia I take to mean a deliberate intervention specifically intended to end a person's life for the purpose of relieving distress. Such intervention may take the indirect form of *assisted suicide*, in which medical staff provide the means to help a patient to end his or her own life. Or it may take the direct form of medical staff themselves ending the life of a compliant or comatose patient.

Euthanasia is said to be *voluntary* when carried out at the request of a fully informed person. *Involuntary* euthanasia describes an act performed without consent. The person killed would be able to express their wishes, but is either not consulted, or is killed despite their desire to go on living. Euthanasia which is *non-voluntary* describes the situation where a person is unable to give consent because of being unconscious, unable to understand the situation, or unable to express their wishes. Proponents of euthanasia stress the essentially voluntary nature of the individual deed, whilst opponents of euthanasia as a matter of public policy predict a tendency for practice to slide from voluntary towards non-voluntary and even involuntary or compulsory killing.

Another distinction which needs to be carefully examined is that between an active intervention which terminates life before it need necessarily come to an end, and a decision to withdraw or withhold treatment in the knowledge that death is likely to ensue. Some argue that there is no logical difference between *killing* and *allowing to die*, but it is possible to marshal a series of arguments which underline the significant moral distinction between accepting the latter whilst rejecting the former.

Robert Veatch lists five persuasive arguments for this distinction.[3] First, there is a psychological difference between the act of killing and a passive decision to let death take place. We feel differently about doing the ultimate deed than about watching nature take its course. Secondly, there is a difference in intention. The whole purpose of killing someone is to bring about their death, whereas the purpose of withdrawing or withholding a treatment is to accept our limitations in respect of the dying process, and to allow the disease to run its course without burdening the patient with inappropriate interventions. Thirdly, there may be wide ranging differences in consequences, not all of which can be foreseen. It is an awfully serious possibility that to allow active killing for mercy will open the door to active killing for less altruistic reasons. These wider consequences cannot be separated from the morality of the individual act. Fourthly, there is a difference in the cause of death, which may have implications for anything from the study of epidemiology to the requirements of life insurance policies. Death by lethal injection is categorically different from death due to advanced and incurable disease. Fifthly, there is a difference in the role of the professional involved. Dating back to the Hippocratic oath, doctors have maintained a professional ethic of

---

3   R Veatch, *Death, Dying and the Biological Revolution* (New Haven: Yale University Press, 1989) pp 61–73.

healing which outlaws any intention to kill. Active killing changes the boundaries of that professional ethic and may deeply undermine the trust that a doctor, approaching the bedside with an injection, is aiming to preserve life rather than to destroy it. The recent murder trial of Dr Harold Shipman has drawn attention to the enormity of that trust which has been vested in doctors for thousands of years.

Taken together, these arguments help to emphasize the moral distinctions which need to be drawn between any active intervention to end life and those decisions which, whilst more frequent, may be no less controversial, in which medical staff withdraw or withhold treatments in order that death may be allowed to take place. I believe that it is confusing and unhelpful to describe such decisions as 'passive euthanasia' when the psychological, intentional, consequential, pathological and professional implications are different from those of so-called 'active' euthanasia.[4]

Treading the Boundaries

As we enter the twenty-first century, euthanasia as an active intervention remains illegal in the majority of countries. The most well known exception is the Netherlands. Although euthanasia remains formally illegal in the Netherlands, it has become increasingly accepted as an allowable practice since the Leeuwarden trial in 1973, when a doctor received a suspended prison sentence for helping her terminally ill mother to die. Confusion over the legality of the practice was clarified in 1984 by a Supreme Court decision on the Alkmaar case. Although euthanasia remains illegal under Article 293 of the Penal Code, and assisted suicide under Article 294, the Dutch Supreme Court ruled that euthanasia may be legally excusable if a physician contravened the law in order to release a patient from intolerable suffering. Under such circumstances they recognized a defence of necessity or of *force majeure*.

The Court made their landmark decision on the basis of a 'conflict of duties.' The doctor who had intentionally killed an elderly patient at her request was considered 'according to responsible medical opinion,' measured by the 'prevailing standards of medical ethics,' to face a situation of 'necessity,' by which, under Article 40, he was entitled to defence against prosecution for his crime.[5]

Since the Alkmaar case, Dutch courts have further debated the criteria under which a defence of necessity may be accepted. These criteria were formulated by the Royal Dutch Medical Association in 1989 in a set of six requirements for permissible euthanasia. The combination of the third and fourth requirements specify the meaning of *force majeure*.

---

4   Within the limits of this booklet, I will not further consider the ethical problems of treatment-limiting decisions. A helpful review of the issues can be found in the British Medical Association's publication, *Withholding and Withdrawing Life-prolonging Medical Treatment* (London: BMJ Books, 1999).

5   *Nederlandse Jurisprudentie*, 1985, 106, pp 451–453.

1. The request for euthanasia must come only from the patient and must be entirely free and voluntary.
2. The patient's request must be well-considered, durable and persistent.
3. The patient must be experiencing intolerable (not necessarily physical) suffering, with no prospect of improvement.
4. Euthanasia must be a last resort. Other alternatives to alleviate the patient's situation must have been considered and found wanting.
5. Euthanasia must be performed by a physician.
6. The physician must consult with an independent physician colleague who has experience in this field.[6]

Alongside these requirements, the authorities placed a procedural safeguard which required doctors to report all cases of euthanasia to the local medical examiner. Under this notification procedure, doctors are prohibited from certifying the death as due to 'natural causes,' but are obliged to call in the examiner who must make an inspection of the body and file a report with the local prosecutor before the body is released to the next of kin for disposal. Needless to say, the inevitable bureaucracy and delay entailed in these procedures have tempted many physicians to disregard the notification procedure, leading to a high level of under-reporting of the practice of euthanasia.

At the time of writing, further efforts are underway to decriminalize euthanasia in the Netherlands. The current bill before parliament will remove the anomaly of allowable crime by setting the defence for euthanasia on a statutory footing. The bill will remove the current obligation for the public prosecution service to consider every case. Provided that doctors report their actions to regional review committees of medical and legal experts, and these committees are satisfied that strict criteria have been met, then doctors will be protected from prosecution.[7] More controversially, the bill provides for minors aged 12 to 15 to become eligible for euthanasia, in line with existing rights for self-determination in respect of other medical treatments. With or without the consent of their parents, a doctor could agree to perform euthanasia on a minor if he or she is convinced that this would 'prevent serious detriment' to the patient.

Liberal practice in the Netherlands has been watched with critical fascination across the world. In Washington State in 1991, and in California in 1992, provisions to legalize euthanasia were defeated by narrow majorities in public referenda. Despite previous opinion polls which had shown a two-thirds majority in favour of voluntary euthanasia, the constitutionally decisive referendum was defeated in each state by just over 50%.

The state of Oregon, however, achieved a majority in favour of new legislation in 1994, when the Death with Dignity Act was approved by a narrow margin of

6   R L Schwartz, 'Euthanasia and Assisted Suicide in the Netherlands' in *Cambridge Quarterly of Health Care Ethics*, 1995, 4, pp 111–121.
7   'Netherlands Publishes Plans for Euthanasia Law' in *British Medical Journal*, 1999, 319, p 467.

53%. This act makes provision for physician-assisted suicide in the case of an adult with six months or less to live. Terminally ill patients are allowed to request in writing a prescription for medications which can be used to end their lives. After a period of delay in which the wider constitutionality of the Act was tested in federal courts, the Oregon measure has been implemented since 1997, and data on the first fifteen reported cases of physician-assisted suicide are now available.[8]

In the strongly libertarian atmosphere of the United States, not everyone has patience with the cautious restrictions of the law. Retired Michigan pathologist Jack Kevorkian has pursued a personal and much-publicised programme of assisted suicide through his 'death machine,' by which he has facilitated the death of over 120 people. In November 1998 he courted prosecution by filming the death of 52-year-old Thomas Youk on prime time television. 'I want to be prosecuted for euthanasia,' he said. 'I am tired of all the hypocrisy. We shall finish this one way or another. This should never be a crime in a society that calls itself enlightened.'[9] After three previous court actions had been dismissed, Kevorkian was this time convicted and imprisoned for second degree murder.

Boundaries in Britain

Less flamboyant, but no less controversial cases have begun to hit the headlines in Britain. In 1992, Dr Nigel Cox was convicted of murder following his administration of a lethal dose of poisonous potassium chloride. His patient, Lilian Boyes, had suffered increasing pain from rheumatoid arthritis for many years. She had no cancer or progressive fatal illness, but her suffering was so intense that she repeatedly begged Dr Cox to kill her. Unable to control her anguish in any other way, Dr Cox finally relented and administered the lethal injection, which he made no attempt to conceal or deny. He was reported by a nurse, convicted of murder, and received a suspended sentence of one year's imprisonment. The General Medical Council reprimanded him, but allowed him to continue in medical practice on condition that he undertook remedial training in the modern management of pain control.[10]

More recently in 1997 Dr David Moor, an outspoken supporter of euthanasia, made comments to the *Sunday Times* claiming that he had helped a large number of patients to die in his 30 years of practice, including two in the previous week.[11] He was subsequently tried for the murder of George Liddell, who had been suffering considerable pain from bowel cancer. Dr Moor had commenced treatment with diamorphine using a regular dose delivered automatically by a syringe driver. The following day, according to newspaper reports,[12] Dr Moor had administered an extra injection of diamorphine, saying to the family that Mr Liddell had now

8   A E Chin, K Hedberg, G K Higginson, D W Fleming, 'Legalized Physician-assisted Suicide in Oregon: The First Year's Experience' in *N Engl J Med*, 1999, 340 pp 577–83.
9   *60 Minutes*, November 1998.
10   C Dyer, 'GMC Tempers Justice with Mercy' in *British Medical Journal*, 1992, 305, p 1311.
11   C Dyer, 'Two Doctors Confess to Helping Patients to Die' in *British Medical Journal*, 1997, 315, p 206.
12   P Johnston , 'Caring Doctors Accused over "Mercy Killing"' in *Daily Telegraph*, 16 April 1999.

only minutes to live and they were to say their goodbyes. Mr Liddell died shortly afterwards. A *post mortem* did not show evidence of sufficient disease to cause his death, and toxicological examination confirmed that the cause of death was opiate poisoning. In the trial, it was alleged that Dr Moor deliberately ended the life of his patient by administering a fatal dose of diamorphine. Despite his previous unguarded remarks to the press, Dr Moor argued in his defence that his intention had not been to kill the patient, but rather to relieve his pain. He took the line of argument which invokes a 'double effect,' claiming that he gave a high dose of diamorphine to relieve his patient's pain knowing he was likely to die, but not knowing for certain that he would die as a consequence. After lengthy consideration, the jury acquitted him of murder, but the judge ordered that he should pay a proportion of the costs because he had brought the prosecution on himself by making 'very silly' remarks to the press and lying to the police.

Both cases drew a swell of sympathy from the general public. Many people were quick to commend the actions of Dr Cox and Dr Moor as fine examples of 'mercy killing' which should never have been brought to trial. Medical opinion was more critical of the precedents set, and concerned at the loose rhetoric of compassion which was applied in situations where neither doctor showed particular competence in dealing with the challenges of major symptom control. In neither case did the doctors seek further advice or a second opinion which might have led to effective interventions to kill the pain, rather than killing the patient.

The debate continues to divide British opinion, and popular polls show a steady increase in support of the right to 'die with dignity.' Research conducted on behalf of the Voluntary Euthanasia Society demonstrates a major shift in favour of new legislation. To the proposal, 'Some people say that the law should allow adults to receive medical help to an immediate peaceful death if they suffer from an incurable physical illness that is intolerable to them, provided they have previously requested such help in writing,' nearly 80% indicated agreement in the latest National Opinion Poll.[13]

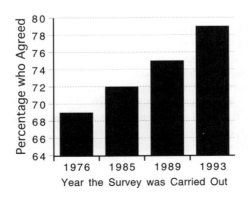

13   Voluntary Euthanasia Society, *Factsheet on Public Opinion* (January 1999).

Not only is the debate within society gathering steam year by year, but there is also pressure within Christian groups for a re-evaluation of traditional moral teaching. Data analysed by Robin Gill from British Social Attitude surveys in the 1980s and 1990s show that support for a change in the law to allow euthanasia to the terminally ill is as prevalent amongst churchgoers as amongst non-churchgoers.[14] More detailed analysis suggests that Roman Catholics express more conservative views than Anglicans, and that core church members from all denominations who attend worship on a weekly basis are less likely to take a liberal view than churchgoers who on average attend only monthly.

Boundaries of Belief

What is the basis of religious objections to this demand for euthanasia? Traditional concerns, voiced by all major religions, spring from a deep sense of the sanctity of life. Human life is a very great gift of God, to be revered, cherished, celebrated and protected from beginning to end. To destroy life is to dishonour the Giver of life.

In the Judeo-Christian tradition, this sense of the awesome value of human life is captured in the idea of the image of God (Genesis 1.26f). Human beings are invested with a unique status within the natural world. The Old Testament theologian, Von Rad, points out that when the image of God is attributed to human beings in the account of Genesis, it is in close connection with human distinctness from and dominion over the rest of the creation. Human lives thus stand in a special and pivotal mid-point between the creation over which they hold sway, and the Creator under whose ultimate providence their lives are shaped.[15]

The paradox of human responsibility reflects this special creaturely relationship to the Creator. On the one hand, human life attains true dignity through learning submission to divine providence. On the other hand, the great dignity of dominion is given to human beings, not least in entrusting them with an awesome degree of freedom and power for self-determination. The twin poles of human responsibility—law and liberty—have clashed throughout the moral history of the Christian faith, often most bitterly over the crucial issues of life and death.

Moral law exists to uphold an essential protective function, requiring that freedom must be exercised within limits. From the ancient injunction to do no murder (Exodus 20.13), Christian teaching has maintained a strict authoritarian line against all unlawful killing. Augustine developed this teaching to condemn suicide, on the grounds that the giving and taking of human life belong to God alone.[16] On this view, human beings act beyond their God-given authority when they presume to determine the span of their own life, or prematurely to bring the life of another person to an end.

Such an authoritarian view of divine sovereignty is entirely alien to modern

---

14   R Gill (ed), *Euthanasia and the Churches* (London: Cassell, 1998) p 19ff.
15   G von Rad, *Theology of the Old Testament* (London: SCM, 1967) p 59ff.
16   Augustine, *The City of God* (Harmondsworth: Penguin, 1972) I 17.

secular thinking, and increasingly unattractive to many contemporary Christian believers. From the time of Augustine onwards, moral theologians have questioned the absolute prohibition of killing by allowing that it may sometimes be justifiable to kill a person under authority. The biblical example of Samson's suicide (Judges 17.28-30) was legitimated by early commentators who believed that God himself had ordered him to pull down the house of Dagon. By an analogous appeal to authority, later Christian teachers supported the killing of warfare, provided that it was pursued under the governance of a just state. Similar arguments have been used to support capital punishment. But such a simple reliance on authority raises enormous questions in a modern democracy. Gill has pointed out that if killing can be justified on the grounds of higher authority, then if euthanasia were to be legalized by majority vote in a particular state it would become morally justifiable for Christian doctors within that state to practise it.[17] The simplistic defence of merely 'acting under orders' presents a dangerously inadequate basis for Christians to contemplate the acceptance of euthanasia.

Another questionable stance which Christians have traditionally been seen to adopt holds that suffering is somehow good for the soul. Allied to a fatalistic belief in divine providence, some Christian teaching has exalted suffering as a scourge sent by God, to be piously endured. *The Book of Common Prayer*, for example, advises that 'there should be no greater comfort to Christian persons than to be made like unto Christ, by suffering patiently adversities, troubles and sicknesses.'[18] It was this thinking that led Victorian Christians to oppose the introduction of anaesthetics. In extolling the virtues of acceptance and courage, some Christians have been markedly short of compassion—particularly when their good advice about patient endurance has been meted out condescendingly to others!

Many Christians now admit that the theological ground in the debate over euthanasia has shifted. Legalistic prohibitions no longer make sense in a society where medical advances have created enormous opportunities for the elimination of unnecessary suffering. The moral teaching of the Bible offers no single absolute value, such as sanctity of life, which can be decisive in every case. An open-minded reading of the gospels shows how Christ himself pushed the boundaries of traditional legalistic morality in the name of a wider compassion. We need to hold all Christian values together—compassion and freedom, justice and peace—in debating the most faithful contemporary way to embrace the responsibilities for life and death for which contemporary medical science equips us.

At the heart of the debate there remains a profoundly serious question about the value and dignity of human life, not merely for individuals, but for a whole society of people bound together in relationships of mutual responsibility. In the chapters that follow, I will explore how a fully Christian ethic of life and death must be inseparable from a richly theological appreciation of the dynamics of human inter-relatedness for the common good.

---

17   R Gill (ed), *Euthanasia and the Churches* (London: Cassell, 1998) p 18.
18   'Order for the Visitation of the Sick' in *The Book of Common Prayer*.

2

Boundaries of Autonomy

The Ultimate Civil Liberty

'But everyone should have the right to die like a gentleman.' So runs the caption on a poster from the Dutch Voluntary Euthanasia Association, neatly expressing the mood of assertiveness and self-determination which insists that human beings have a right to choose the time and the manner of their dying. Autonomy, it is argued, is an essential aspect of human dignity. Each person has the right to choose what happens to his or her own body, and ought to be allowed the freedom to exercise that right. This is the familiar liberal appeal to the so-called 'right to die.'

For advocates of voluntary euthanasia, autonomy is the central moral issue. 'Autonomy is based on the conviction that human dignity lies in being the bearer of basic rights and freedoms, especially the freedom to make of ourselves what we want to be by deciding according to our own values and plans. Anything that stands in the way of "free choice" assaults personal dignity.'[19]

Not only is autonomy a right, it can also be presented as a responsibility. Hans Küng writes as a revisionist Catholic theologian that life, which is a gift from God, is also a human task and responsibility. This demands an 'autonomy based on theonomy.'[20] For Küng, it is callous and sub-Christian to deny euthanasia in the face of a life which is reduced to intolerable suffering.

The rationale of free choice emphasizes individual values and differences. What one person may tolerate in the way of suffering is entirely unacceptable to another. The value of autonomy upholds the right and responsibility for each individual to make personal decisions about quality of life. Pain may not be the only issue, perhaps not even a major issue in end-of-life decisions. Far more important may be a person's evaluation of their quality of life. People do not want to spend the last days or weeks of their life in a way which, *to them*, is undignified, even if caring professionals are quick to relieve their symptoms of physical distress.

---

19   R M Gula, *Euthanasia: Moral and Pastoral Perspectives* (New York: Paulist Press, 1994) p 8.
20   H Küng, W Jens, *A Dignified Dying: A Plea for Personal Responsibility* (London: SCM, 1995).

Pain and Dignity

Annie Lindsell, suffering from end-stage motor neurone disease in 1997, spoke up for many: 'The hospice movement consistently maintains that in most cases it manages the pain of terminally ill patients. What they cannot control, however, is the loss of personal dignity and that is a very individual criterion that no-one but the patient can comment on.'[21] Ms Lindsell campaigned for two years through the courts for the use of drugs to shorten her life. Having seen friends die of the condition, she did not want to go through the final stages choking on her food and unable to speak. In the event, no special permission was given, or needed, since doctors have always been allowed to use appropriate drugs to relieve distress. The High Court was able to clarify that the use of pain-killing drugs proposed by her GP in the event of overwhelming distress was in line with good medical practice and skilful palliative care. When the terminal stage came, Ms Lindsell died peacefully at home without any need of drugs. Her doctor commented that she had been able to die 'in dignified autonomy' because she knew he could help if necessary. 'She knew the choice was available. She didn't want me to kill her, she wanted every last minute of life, she loved life.'[22]

Like many people who are appalled at the prospect of progressive physical or mental deterioration, Annie Lindsell needed some sense of control over her life and death in order to maintain a measure of human dignity. Her battle for legally assisted dying was a powerful assertion of individual autonomy and her desire to make informed choices up to the very end of life. She epitomised the struggle of individuals who feel impotent in the face of entrenched conservatism in the combined forces of medicine and the law. For them, the right to self-determination is a critically important civil liberty.

Christians cannot ignore these moral and democratic concerns for personal autonomy. Too often, religious conservatism has colluded with the paternalism of powerful doctors and lawyers in silencing the valid demand that human beings should make their own judgments concerning quality of life. It is hardly surprising that the mood of consumerism in contemporary society supports patients who question whether 'doctor knows best' when their pleas for a peaceful exit seem to be systematically ignored.

Human dignity and human freedom are vital elements in a fully Christian ethic of life and death which entrusts individuals with enormous powers of choice, for good and ill. Within a religious framework which respects the life of each individual as a uniquely precious gift of God, autonomy is a fundamentally important ethical principle. Yet it is not the only value which needs to be upheld in a difficult and many-sided public debate.

---

21 A Lindsell, quoted in *The Case For*, Voluntary Euthanasia Society Factsheet (October 1999).
22 'Motor Neuron Victim Dies with Dignity at Home' in *The Times*, December 1997.

One Man's Freedom...

The problem with euthanasia is that it can never be a matter of purely private morality. All human individuals have distinct and personal needs which must be respected alongside the different, and possibly conflicting, needs of other members of society. We are so bound together within complex networks of relationships that any decision about an individual life will bear upon the lives of many others amongst whom we live. A Christian view of life respects all the organic relationships between human beings in community as reflecting the loving exchange of dignity and delight that exists at the heart of God-in-Trinity. For this reason, what is loving and merciful to any individual cannot be separated from what may be dangerous or dehumanizing to another. Compassion cannot be separated from justice, or freedom from responsibility.

It is for this reason that Christians have been deeply concerned about the social consequences of euthanasia. Can we be sure that a law to allow mercy-killing will not be open to abuse? Would doctors, given the option to offer euthanasia, try a little less hard to deal with difficult pain and symptoms? Might some families, burdened by months and years of caring, quietly encourage the relative who 'no longer wants to be a burden' to seek a legitimate way out? And since the difference between murder and euthanasia would simply be a matter of intention, could the public properly be protected against the deceitfulness of plausible criminals like Dr Harold Shipman?

If any liberalization of the practice of euthanasia were to be allowed, then it would be essential for stringent checks and safeguards to prevent the potential for unlimited abuse, coercion and deceit. Killing is a uniquely final act. There is no possibility to appeal, after the event, that the person may have changed their mind, or that something more could have been done, or that further help might have been offered to protect a very vulnerable human being.

Campaigners for euthanasia claim that careful legislation could provide all the necessary safeguards. They look admiringly to the liberalization that has been achieved in the Netherlands with the full backing of professional medical bodies who have worked with lawyers to refine the necessary procedural regulations. Surely it is not beyond the wit of law-makers to formulate adequate and accountable tests which will distinguish between justifiable and unjustifiable homicide?

The Problem in Practice

Unfortunately, the application of safeguards is not so simple in practice. 'The Cartesian assumption that clarity, order, and pre-established procedure will govern the practice of euthanasia, and will do so successfully, floats in abstraction above the real world in which euthanasia will be practised.'[23] People who work with the terminally ill report that requests for euthanasia are often short-lived,

---

23 D Roy, N MacDonald, in Doyle, Hanks and MacDonald (eds), *Oxford Textbook of Palliative Medicine* (Oxford University Press, 1998) p 128.

and rarely sustained after good symptom control is established.[24] More often, a request for euthanasia is voiced by a carer or relative, whose own distress is the source of a pressure which the patient might not feel for themselves. Still more worrying are the pervasive economic pressures in a society where the financial burden of caring for increasing numbers of elderly and dependent people generates a further dynamic by which euthanasia could be welcomed as a highly cost-effective choice. Against subtle pressures from professional and family carers, and the less subtle debate about allocation of scarce resources in a society greedy for health expenditure, it is easy to imagine that a vulnerable person could be swayed to accept euthanasia, almost as a public duty.

Are such concerns unduly cynical, or is there empirical evidence that the availability of euthanasia shifts the practice unavoidably in the direction of less than fully voluntary choice? Sadly, all evidence from the Netherlands points unambiguously in the direction of a steady shift. Data received by the Remmelink commission in 1991 on the extent and nature of medical euthanasia practice revealed an alarmingly high level of interventions to hasten the end of life. John Keown has critically reviewed this data and demonstrated the high proportion of end-of-life decisions which were implemented with no explicit consent from the patient.[25] In the year 1990, the recorded number of cases of euthanasia and assisted suicide was 8,900 and 400 respectively, accounting together for 1.6% of all deaths in the Netherlands. In almost half the cases of euthanasia the patient's life was terminated without request.

Such statistics are deeply disturbing. The abuse which they reveal is only the tip of the iceberg, however, since there is extensive evidence of unreported euthanasia and a widespread approach to the use of painkilling drugs which advocates unnecessarily high doses as a cloak for undeclared and unjustified euthanasia.[26]

An Easy Way Out

The acceptance of euthanasia by the Dutch legislature has shifted the boundaries of professional ethics and changed the moral temperature of a whole society. The effects can be illustrated by typical case histories which reveal the dangers of looking to euthanasia as an easy way out of challenging situations.[27]

A patient with disseminated breast cancer had severe pain. Morphine was administered by injection once or twice a day and the dose was increased every 2 days in an endeavour to achieve relief. Eventually, she was receiving

---

24 Association for Palliative Medicine, *Submission to the Select Committee of the House of Lords on Medical Ethics* (May 1993).

25 J Keown (ed), *Euthanasia Examined: Ethical, Clinical and Legal Perspectives* (Cambridge University Press, 1995) p 266ff.

26 A survey in Amsterdam showed that over two thirds of GP's in the Netherlands had certified a patient as having died from natural causes when in fact they had helped the patient to commit suicide (Reported in *British Medical Journal*, 1992, 304, p 462).

27 Z Zylich, quoted in J Keown (ed), *Euthanasia Examined: Ethical, Clinical and Legal Perspectives* (Cambridge University Press, 1995) p 160f.

more than 2g of morphine a day but was still in pain. Several weeks previously, at a hospital outpatient visit, she told the doctor she would never choose euthanasia because of her beliefs. She was admitted under the care of the same doctor and treated with intravenous midazolam and morphine. She became unconscious, so the dose of midazolam was decreased. She woke up and stated she was free of pain. She said goodbye to her family and to the doctor. After a weekend on duty, the doctor went home at 0900 on the Monday morning. She died 30 minutes later. Next day, a junior nurse told the weekend duty doctor that another doctor had ordered a twenty-fold increase in the dose of morphine. Her family had been asked to leave the room. The order was given verbally and the doctor refused to confirm it in writing. When the doctor was challenged by the weekend duty doctor he replied, 'It could have taken another week before she died: I just needed this bed.'

An old man was dying from disseminated lung cancer. His symptoms were well controlled and he asked if he could go and die at home. When his four children were told about his wish, they would not agree to take care of him. Even after repeated discussion, they refused. Instead, they pointed to their father's suffering and the need to finish things quickly 'in the name of humanity.' When the doctor refused, they threatened to sue him. Because the patient insisted on going home, a social worker went to investigate. She discovered that the patient's house was empty and that every piece of furniture had been taken by the family.

Such reports are not isolated cases of abuse. Numerous medical colleagues from the Netherlands tell of cynical or utilitarian attitudes cloaked by a veneer of humanitarianism which justifies a resort to euthanasia at the slightest sign of difficulty in dealing with terminal care. Berthus van Dijk recalled his first experience of medical intervention at the end of life when, as a junior doctor, he witnessed an anaesthetist marching down the ward with an injection for an elderly lady. 'That difficult case at the end of the ward will not be a medical problem for much longer,' he declared. The patient died ten minutes later.[28]

In quoting such unsavoury examples, I have no wish to cast aspersions on the conscientious work of many Dutch physicians who practice euthanasia entirely as a last resort, and with a very heavy heart.[29] They have little alternative. Sadly, the provision of palliative care in the Netherlands is woefully inadequate, and the availability of expertise in pain and symptom control is limited to major centres. In a recent report to the House of Lords, Dr Ben Zylich suggested that the fact that there were only 70 specialist palliative care beds in the whole country was the chief reason why doctors resorted to euthanasia.[30] 'If you accept euthanasia as a

28 B van Dijk, address to the Royal College of Physicians (November 1999).
29 A more positive evaluation of the Dutch experience is given by Ruurd Veldhuis in 'Tired of Living,
    Afraid of Dying' in *Studies in Christian Ethics*, 1998, 11 (1), pp 63–76.
30 H Matthews, 'Better Palliative Care Could Cut Euthanasia' in *British Medical Journal*, 1998, 317, p 1613.

solution to difficult and unresolved problems in palliative care, you will never learn anything,' he warned. Euthanasia has become a short cut. Since few doctors receive any training in palliative medicine, they often feel that they have no other options if a patient's suffering becomes too great for their skills to control. It is not their compassion that is lacking, as much as specialist knowledge and the availability of appropriate, albeit expensive, facilities.

Learning from Experience

It is important that other European countries should learn from the experience of the Netherlands, and weigh very carefully the likely consequences of any liberalization of the law. 'If ever there was a case for looking before we leap, then this is it.'[31] There is undeniable evidence of procedural deterioration, of professional disillusionment and of growing public anxiety about the liberal practice of medical euthanasia.

Commentators in Britain have likened these developments to the consequences of legalized abortion. As far back as 1974, Dr John Habgood sounded a warning note. 'Legislation to permit euthanasia would in the long run bring about profound changes in social attitudes towards death, illness, old age and the role of the medical profession. The Abortion Act has shown what happens. Whatever the rights and wrongs concerning the present practice of abortion, there is no doubt about two consequences of the 1967 Act:

(a) The safeguards and assurances given when the Bill was passed have to a considerable extent been ignored.
(b) Abortion has now become a live option [sic] for *anybody* who is pregnant. This does not imply that everyone who is facing an unwanted pregnancy automatically attempts to procure an abortion. But because abortion is now on the agenda, the climate of opinion in which such a pregnancy must be faced has radically altered.

One could expect similarly far-reaching and potentially more dangerous consequences from legalized euthanasia.'[32]

Just as doctors in Britain now find it difficult to get jobs in gynaecology if they conscientiously object to abortion,[33] the experience of Dutch doctors is that general practitioners are unlikely to find a post in group practices unless they are prepared to take on their share of euthanasia.[34] Amongst the general public, fear of unwarranted euthanasia means that 10,000 people now carry anti-euthanasia 'passports,' because they are frightened of being killed prematurely if they fall ill. The 'declaration of life' card says: 'I request that no medical treatment be withheld on the grounds that the future quality of my life will be diminished, because

---

31 J Keown (ed), *Euthanasia Examined: Ethical, Clinical and Legal Perspectives* (CUP, 1995) p xv.
32 J Habgood, 'Euthanasia—A Christian View' in *Journal of the Royal Society of Health*, 1974, 124, p 126.
33 C Flynn, 'A Right to Refuse' in *BMA News Review*, September 1999, p 18.
34 L Wolbert, personal communication.

I believe that this is not something that human beings can judge. I request that under no circumstances a life-ending treatment be administered because I am of the opinion that people do not have the right to end life.'[35]

The impact of legalized euthanasia in the Netherlands has been enormous. Polish philosopher Kolakowski argues that the unique and irreplaceable character of each human being has long been a fundamental value throughout European culture. To undermine this value in any society by accepting that it can be right or convenient to kill certain people is tantamount to 'cultural suicide.'[36] The sweeping social consequences of euthanasia are immensely more serious than any simple argument from autonomy might suggest.

No Man is an Island

In Christian ethics, one of the chief criteria for a 'good' society is the protection that it affords to its most vulnerable members. God himself is recognized as the defender of the defenceless (Psalm 10.14), and he judges the nations on the basis of their care for the weak (Isaiah 10.1–2).

This insight is enshrined in the moral principle of the 'common good,' which has been widely promoted through a recent teaching document from the Roman Catholic church.[37] The principle of the common good challenges the anti-social tendencies of unbounded individual freedom. 'If we put too much emphasis on autonomy, we fail to realize that any changes in our social relationships can change the way we develop. In this light, we can appreciate the Catholic moral tradition's insistence that the communal aspect of life must be structured to support the dignity of each person. Thus, any expression of personal freedom must be assessed with its social implications. This holds for the way that we die, too. For the way we die is shaped by, and, in turn, shapes our relationships with others. Therefore, euthanasia must be scrutinized in light of communal values and commitments.'[38]

When the practice of euthanasia is scrutinized in the light of the common good, then a number of major concerns become apparent. What would be the effect on elderly and disabled members of society? 'The sense that they were unwanted, a burden to their families and a cost to society, would undermine their self-worth. Today's right to die would become tomorrow's duty to die.'[39]

How could large numbers of mentally impaired older and younger people be protected from the sacrifice of their own autonomy to the more powerful utilitarian claims of those who might judge their lives 'not worth living'? And how could we sustain a compassionate commitment to the care of the suffering and the dy-

35 'Dutch Carry Card That Says: Don't Kill Me, Doctor' in *Sunday Telegraph*, 18th October 1998.
36 L Kolakowski, 'Het doden van gehandicapte kinderen als het fundamentele probleem van de filosofie' (The killing of handicapped children as the fundamental problem of philosophy) in *Rekenschap*, 1972, 19, pp 35–49.
37 *The Common Good and the Catholic Church's Social Teaching* (A Statement by the Catholic Bishops' Conference of England and Wales, 1997).
38 R M Gula, *Euthanasia: Moral and Pastoral Perspectives* (New York: Paulist Press, 1994) p 15.
39 Cardinal B Hume, 'The Death of Trust' in *Church Times*, 27th November 1997.

ing if euthanasia were legalized and were to appear the 'cost-effective' option? Up to 90% of the hospital resources of the NHS are spent on patients in their last months of life. 'The economic attractions of euthanasia are obvious. It would be a very dangerous and insidious temptation.'[40]

Richard Gula reminds us that the biblical commandment which prohibits murder must be read alongside the previous commandment to 'honour your father and your mother' (Exodus 20.12–13). 'We miss the significance of this commandment if we understand it as requiring children to obey their parents. The original commandment was addressed to an adult community that was easily tempted, as a nomadic people, to leave behind or neglect anyone who was aged, feeble, senile, or useless in favour of clan members with greater mobility and vitality. This commandment indicates that human honour and worth are innate to our relation to God and to others who are interdependent partners with us in a covenantal community. Within covenantal bonds, honour and worth are not dependent on social usefulness.'[41]

The boundaries of autonomy are the limits of freedom and responsibility accepted within a community of care. Beyond the clamant individualism of the contemporary moral debate, we need to keep sight of an earlier world view expressed by the 17th century poet:

> 'No man is an island, entire of itself;
> every man is a piece of the continent, a part of the main.
> If a clod be washed away by the sea, Europe is the less…
> Any man's death diminishes me
> because I am involved in mankind,
> and therefore never send to know for whom the bell tolls;
> it tolls for thee.'[42]

---

40   *Ibid.*
41   R M Gula, *Euthanasia: Moral and Pastoral Perspectives* (New York: Paulist Press, 1994) p 27.
42   J Donne, 'Meditation XVII' from *Norton Anthology of English Literature* (New York: Norton and Co, 1986) p 528.

3

Boundaries of Compassion

Counting the Cost

The core of my argument in this booklet is that a society which restricts the boundaries of individual autonomy in respect of euthanasia must be ready to stretch out its boundaries of compassion towards those who cry for an end to their distress. The debate about euthanasia is not an armchair exercise for abstract theorists. It is a deeply practical challenge to our humanity and our commitment to mutual care. Without adequate care, the anguished appeal for euthanasia on the grounds of compassion has no humane response. 'You wouldn't let a dog go on suffering like this—would you?'

It is illusory to imagine that the distress which motivates requests for euthanasia can be easily relieved. Downing emphasized that we shall probably never be able to eliminate totally from human experience the suffering that is both hard to bear and hard to behold.[43] The intensity of this suffering may be physical or mental, social or spiritual, and it is often most cruelly combined in those who are already disadvantaged in life. For them and their families, exhausted, bewildered, guilt-ridden and without help, the cost of continued caring may be impossibly beyond their reach. Would it not be a 'mercy' to bring their anguish to an end?

The Christian vision of 'mercy' points us away from any convenient short cuts. The 'mercy' which is an unfailing characteristic of God speaks of costly and continued faithfulness. 'God's mercy is the fulfilment of the covenantal commitment to be with and for the chosen people in all circumstances. Mercy and compassion are the ways that God, who had covenanted with Israel, continues to love her, provides for her, and protects her from harm. Mercy is always available to the people of the covenant because of God's faithfulness to them. In the life of Jesus, mercy and compassion led him to do works which restored the broken to wholeness. Out of mercy and compassion, he healed the blind (Matthew 20.34), taught the ignorant (Mark 6.34), raised the dead (Luke 7.13) and fed the hungry (Matthew 15.32).[44] Supremely, he showed mercy by taking upon himself the pain of human suffering and death (Hebrews 2.14–18; 4.15–16).

A compassionate response to the distress that demands euthanasia does not lie in so-called 'mercy-killing,' which solves the problem of caring by ceasing to care. A truly Christian response requires us to count the cost of embracing profound distress with serious commitment and skilled companionship.

---

43 A B Downing (ed), *Euthanasia and the Right to Death* (London: Peter Owen, 1969) p 23.
44 R M Gula, *Euthanasia: Moral and Pastoral Perspectives* (New York: Paulist Press, 1994) p 41.

Painstaking Palliative Care

The hospice movement has wrestled with what that serious commitment and skilled companionship must entail. Energetic research into the cause and treatment of pain and major symptoms has produced remarkable progress. Therapeutic advances and access to specialist skills mean that the overwhelming majority of patients treated by a palliative care team can expect either very good, or certainly 'good enough,' control of their physical symptoms.

All this can be achieved without resort to dangerously high doses of drugs. Modern methods of drug administration which carefully titrate the dose and delivery of potent medicines, according to the hour by hour response of a patient, allow for precise individualization of treatment regimes. With newly developed drugs and combinations of drugs, even the most intractable symptoms can now be effectively controlled without excessive side effects.

Such expertise calls into question the appeal to a 'double effect' principle which has been used in the past to defend doctors whose zealous use of sedatives and analgesic drugs has, perhaps unintentionally, advanced death. There is considerable confusion in the public mind about the use of drugs such as morphine and diamorphine, and many myths still persist amongst professionals. One of the greatest challenges for palliative medicine is to disseminate a more modern and sophisticated understanding of these valuable drugs so that patients and their families can expect proper pain relief without any suspicion of ulterior intent.[45]

Whatever the rights and wrongs of a 'double effect' defence in relation to past practices, the pursuit of excellence in modern palliative medicine should have the single intention of helping people to live as well as possible for as long as possible.

Learning to Listen

'Total pain' is the vivid phrase coined by Cicely Saunders to convey the overwhelming experience of suffering in which many dimensions of distress—physical and practical, spiritual and existential, emotional and psychological, social and economic—may cruelly coincide.[46] The challenge of caring for someone in the darkness of 'total pain' should not be underestimated. Families, friends and professional carers will be asked personally to absorb some of this pain. *Compassion*, after all, means *suffering-with.*

Attentive listening must be the foundation for total care, and is an essential first step in alleviating the anguish of those who want to die. Ben Zylich has painstakingly catalogued the concerns voiced by patients in his Dutch hospice who request euthanasia.[47] Without striving to understand their distress, it would be arrogant to presume to help them. His research has suggested a model for respecting and supporting people who plead to make an end of things. Their concerns can be categorized under five broad headings.

45 'Double Effect, Double Bind or Double Speak?' Editorial in *Palliative Medicine*, 1999, 13, pp 365–366.
46 C Saunders, *The Management of Terminal Disease* (London: Edward Arnold, 1978) pp 194–5.
47 Z Zylich, *Dealing with Patients who Request Euthanasia in Hospice Environment* (Lecture delivered to European Association of Palliative Care Congress, September 1999).

A) The largest group (80% of patients) are afraid. They may have had bad experiences in the past related to poor symptom control and horrible dying. Often they are afraid of things that will never happen. Many of these people are also old and frail, and are afraid or embarrassed to become a burden. They are immeasurably helped by care and reassurance. Most of them do not want to die at all, and once a trusting relationship has been established, and they are offered continuing care and attention, their desire for euthanasia evaporates. In British experience, this same group of anxious patients predominate. They are the people who are overwhelmingly grateful for the kindness and security that hospice care provides.

B) A significant minority (around 5%) are described as burnt out. They have undergone intensive treatment with punishing chemotherapy or mutilating surgery, and their emotional resources are spent. Although they may be in remission from their illness, they feel they have lost the will to go on. In the Netherlands, Zylich argues that the availability of euthanasia is an option which compounds their existential suffering. In Britain, this group of patients, many of them young and articulate, some of them people with AIDS, look for peer support and unpatronizing professional empathy as they struggle to rehabilitate after an intensely damaging period of their lives.

C) A few patients (only 1% in Zylich's hospice) are described as control orientated. They are usually young, and may not have physical problems as much as a deep-seated need to stay in control, ready to meet potential suffering with decisive action. They dread dependency. Their concerns are self-oriented, and may either disregard or even conflict with the desires of their families. In the Netherlands, such people avoid hospices, preferring to make an agreement with their GP about euthanasia. The British situation is different, but Zylich's control-orientated type can be recognized in the vocal minority of public activists for euthanasia. They demand choice, and assert their autonomy. Because British law maintains a firm line against euthanasia, doctors can often help these people by exploring alternative strategies which offer maximum control within the boundaries of the law, and with respect to the impact of decisions on other people. Sensitive spiritual care may unearth the deeper insecurities that lie beneath an aggressively controlling attitude, and occasionally leads to a breakthrough of new trust and unexpected hopefulness.

D) An important group of patients are clinically depressed. Zylich reports up to 10% in this category, but British and American studies suggest that unrecognized depression is a major and treatable factor in many people who give up hope.[48] Such people may have suffered depression in the past, and often have fewer psychological resources, and adapt poorly to their illness. In this respect, they may overlap with some patients in category (B). It is important to have a low threshold for treating depression in patients with major physical

---

48 J H Brown et al, 'Is it Normal for Terminally Ill Patients to Desire Death?' in *American Journal of Psychiatry,* 1986, 143, pp 208–211.

illness. Not only are modern antidepressant drugs immensely helpful, but non-pharmacological treatments ranging from massage to art therapy, self-help groups to cognitive therapy may also have a dramatic impact in overcoming the depths of despair. In British experience, an element of depression is prevalent in a majority of dying patients, especially those who have to give up the independence of their own homes. In restoring their dignity, and providing the hospitable warmth of a hospice environment, the emotional needs of such vulnerable people can be greatly eased.

E) A small group of patients (4%) present with extreme and intractable difficulties. Such patients are a challenge, even to specialist units, because of the severity of their symptoms, or the complexity of their personal situations. Some may be fiercely uncooperative. Others may have appalling family relationships. They make intense, seemingly unreasonable demands on the whole professional team. In hospice work, careful communication and patient teamwork is essential in lowering the emotional temperature generated by such extreme cases. Occasionally, the distress may be so intractable that a resort to mild sedation is justifiable, if only to give respite to family members who have come to the end of their tether.

These are the actualities of a compassionate approach to palliative care, which is committed to struggling *with* the patient's distress, rather than seeking a way out through euthanasia. In Britain, the hospice approach, with its sensitivity to the many dimensions of human distress, is gaining ground in all areas of health care, and has done much to prevent a euthanasia mentality from gaining ground.

Actions Speak Louder than Words

'When someone asks for euthanasia or turns to suicide, I believe in almost every case someone or society as a whole has failed that person.'[49] Cicely Saunders, by inspiring world-wide enthusiasm for the hospice philosophy, has done more than any single individual to provide a positive alternative to euthanasia.

That alternative has been promoted, not by wordy and moralizing campaigns, but through the commitment of hundreds of local charities who have urged their communities to go the second mile in providing decent facilities for the dying. The continued development of the hospice approach, not merely in specialist centres which care for a tiny minority of people, but extending into the training of all doctors and nurses, and ensuring the provision of proper community support as well as the rare luxury of admission to a hospice bed, is an essential, though expensive, public priority.

---

49   C Saunders, 'Caring to the End' in *Nursing Mirrors*, 4, September 1980.

4
Conclusion

Christians have no right to impose their own moral commitments and beliefs on other members of a pluralist society. They do have a duty to contribute to the ongoing debate, which is essential in every society that seeks to know what it stands for, and what it stands against. At the end of the day, compassionate witness is more compelling than argument, and the commitment of Christians to the development of a caring community is the best possible counter to the dangerous demands for euthanasia.

The unspoken message of the gospel is addressed to every individual who is met with caring and faithful commitment:

> 'You matter because you are you.
> You matter to the last moment of your life,
> and we will do all we can,
> not only to help you die peacefully,
> but to live until you die.'[50]

---

50   C Saunders, quoted in *Mud and Stars* (Oxford: Sobell Publications, 1991) p 10.